SEESAW

Selected and Edited by
LELAND B. JACOBS

and

JO JASPER TURNER

A Beka Book®
A MINISTRY OF
Pensacola Christian College
PENSACOLA, FLORIDA 32523-9160

A Beka Book® Reading Program

Basic Phonics Program
Speed Reading and Comprehension Skill Sheets
Primary Bible Reader

CONTENTS

COUNTING TIME

Illustrated by June Goldsborough and Richard Scarry

RUN, JUMP, AND GO

Illustrated by Bernice Myers

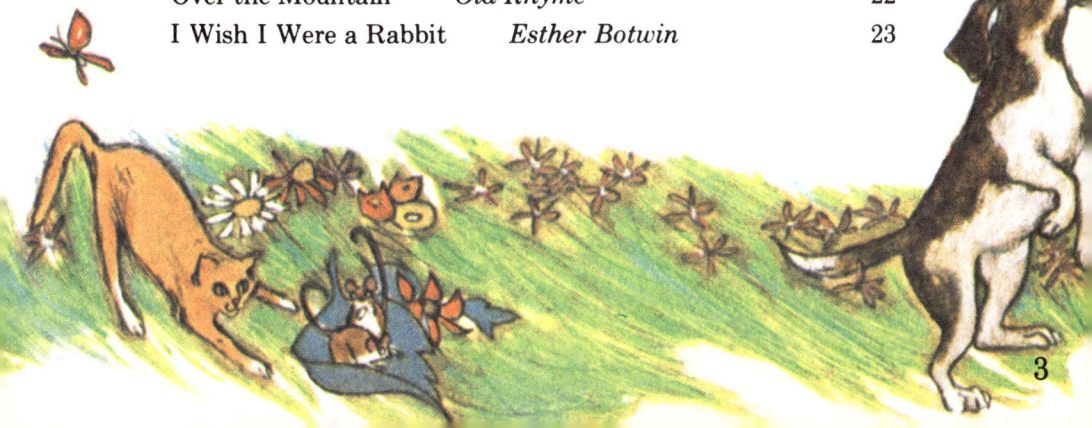

SEE AND SAY

Illustrated by Trina Hyman, John Miller, Alice and Martin Provensen, Bernice Myers, and Gloria Gaulke

ANIMAL TALK

Illustrated by Barbara Werner, Gloria Gaulke,
Trina Hyman, and Irma Wilde

STORY PEOPLE

Illustrated by Sheilah Beckett, Carol Wilde,
and Hertha Depper

THE ALPHABET

Illustrated by William J. Dugan

Counting Time

Count the flowers.
Count the bees.
Count the jets
Above the trees.
Count the children
At the door.
Count and count
and count some more.

Counting

1   2   3   4   5
I caught a hare alive.

6   7   8   9   10
I let it go again.

Umbrellas

1 umbrella,

2 umbrellas,

3 umbrellas gay!

Down the street
They go like flowers
On a rainy day.

Two Little Birds

Two little birds
Were sitting on a wall,
One named Peter,
One named Paul.

Fly away, Peter,
Fly away, Paul.
Come back, Peter,
Come back, Paul.

Jumps

One jump,
we'll jump to the moon,

Two jumps,
we'll jump to a star—

Three and four
and one or two more
And we won't know where we are!

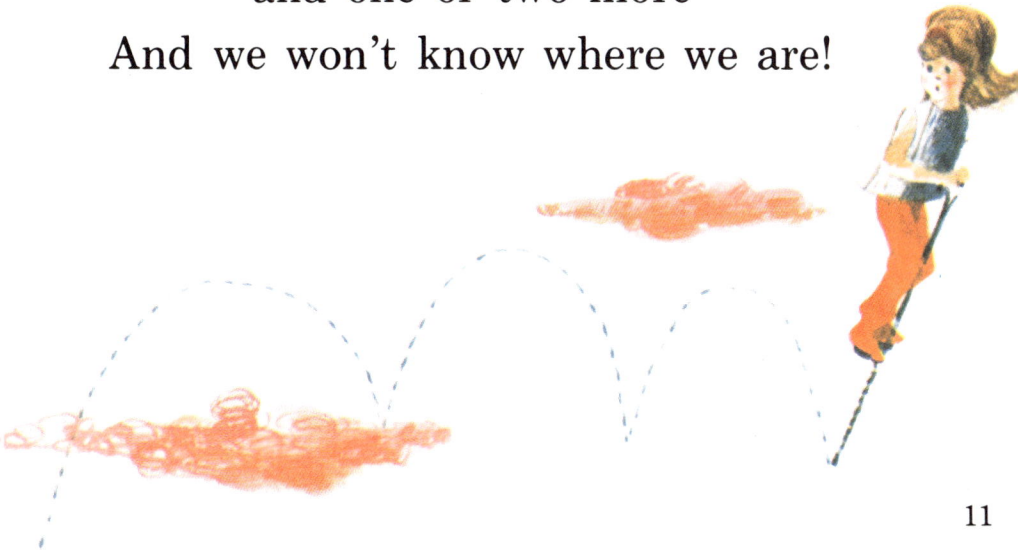

Box Fun

One box makes a car.
Beep! Beep!

Two boxes make a dump truck.
Boom!

Three boxes make an airplane.
Zoom!

Four boxes make a train.
Toot! Toot!

Five boxes make a boat.
Hurrah! Hurrah!

Six boxes make a caterpillar.
Humpety, humpety, hump.

Five Little Yellow Birds

Five little yellow birds
Were singing at the door.
One flew away
And then there were four.

Four little yellow birds
Were singing for me.
One flew away
And then there were three.

Three little yellow birds
Were singing for you.
One flew away
And then there were two.

Two little yellow birds
Were singing in the sun.
One flew away
And then there was one.

One little yellow bird
Was singing at the door.
One flew away—
There aren't any more.

Ten Little Indians

1 little,
2 little,
3 little Indians,

4 little,
5 little,
6 little Indians,

7 little,
8 little,
9 little Indians,

10 little Indian boys.

10 little,
 9 little,
 8 little Indians,

  7 little,
  6 little,
  5 little Indians,

   4 little,
   3 little,
   2 little Indians,

1 little Indian boy.

Twenty's Plenty

One — two — three — four,
  No! there are five.
No! there are more.

Six — seven — eight — nine
  Little ducklings in a line.

Ten — eleven — twelve —
  TWENTY!
  Twenty's lots.
Twenty's plenty!

Run, Jump, and Go

Here we go up, up, up.
Here we go down, down, downy.
Here we go backwards and forwards.
And here we go round, round, roundy.

Up and Down and Over

A butterfly
Came dancing by,
Up and down and over,
Up and down,
Up and down,
Up and down and over.

A honey bee
Came dancing free,
Up and down and over,
Up and down,
Up and down,
Up and down and over.

A honey bee
And butterfly,
Up and down and over,
Danced and danced
As they came by,
Then rested in the clover.

Over the Mountain

The bear went over the mountain,
The bear went over the mountain,
The bear went over the mountain
    To see what he could see.

The other side of the mountain,
The other side of the mountain,
The other side of the mountain
    Was all that he could see.

I Wish I Were a Rabbit

I wish I were a rabbit,

a rabbit,

a rabbit.

I wish I were a rabbit.
I know what I would do.

I'd go like this—hop-hop, hop-hop!
I'd go like this—hop-hop, hop-hop!
I'd go like this—hop-hop, hop-hop!

And that's what I would do.

Balls

Red balls,

Blue balls,

Big balls,

Little balls!

Throw them!
Roll them!
That is easy!

Red balls,
Blue balls,
Big balls,
Little balls!

Try to catch them!
That is hard!

Jumping

Jump-jump-jump!
  Jump over the moon.
Jump all the morning,
  And all the noon.

Jump-jump-jump!
  Jump far away,
And all come home
  Some other day.

Seesaw

Up and down,
Up and down,
Seesaws pop
Up.
Seesaws drop
Down.

The down is a bump.
The up is a jump.
Seesaw,
Seesaw,
Up!

Snowy Morning

Everywhere
I walk
And go,
I leave
My
Step-marks
In
The
Snow.

Sliding

We can slide

       down

          the

             hill

or

    down

       the

         stair

or

    down

       the

         street

or anywhere.

Or down the roof
   where the shingles broke,
Or down the trunk
   of the back-yard oak.

Down
   the
      slide
         or the ice
         or the slippery
         street,

We can slide on our sled

or our skates

or our feet.

Oh, it's lots of fun to go outside

And slide

and slide

and slide

and slide.

On Top

Wherever I am
I never stop,
Trying to climb
To get on top.

On top the bed,
    On top the chair,
I cannot wait
    To see what's there.

32

I'm never happy
Unless I try
To reach the top,
No matter how high.

When I grow up,
Will I ever stop,
Or still keep trying
To reach the top?

I Wish I Had

I haven't got a puppy-dog.
I wish I had a puppy-dog,
So I pretend my puppy-dog
Is trotting after me!

I haven't got a sailing-ship.
I wish I had a sailing-ship,
So I pretend my sailing-ship
Is sailing on the sea!

I haven't got an airplane.
I wish I had an airplane,
So I pretend my airplane
Is flying in the sky!

I haven't got a pony-cart.
I wish I had a pony-cart,
So I pretend my pony-cart
Will be here by-and-by!

The Little Man
Who Wasn't There

As I was going up the stair,
I met a man who wasn't there.
He wasn't there again today!
I wish, I wish
He'd stay away.

See and Say

See and say your letters—
A and B and C.

See and say your numbers—
1 and 2 and 3.

See and say your colors—
Green and blue and gray.

There are oh so many things
You can see and say.

Who Are We?

Who are YOU?

Are you a cake?

Are you a rake?

Are you a lake?

Not a cake,
Not a rake,
Not a lake—

You are YOU.

Who am I?

Am I a book?

Am I a hook?

Am I a brook?

Not a book,
Not a hook,
Not a brook—

I am ME.

I am ME.

You are
YOU.

We are WE.
YOU and ME.

The Neck

The neck
Of a calf
Is a half
Of a half
Of a half
Of a half
Of a half
Of a half
Of a half

Of the size
Of the neck
Of a little
Giraffe.

Ride a Horse

Mother rides a white horse,
Father rides a brown,
Rides, rides, rides, rides,
All the way to town.

Sister rides a gray horse,
Brother rides a black,
Rides, rides, rides, rides,
Into town and back.

A-B-C

A, B, C, and tumble-down D,
I fell out of the cherry tree.
Why did the tree do that to me?
A, B, C, and tumble-down D.

A, B, C, and tumble-down D,
I got tumbled by the sea.
Why did the sea do that to me?
A, B, C, and tumble-down D.

A, B, C, and tumble-down D,
I sat down on a bumblebee.
Why did the bee do that to me?
A, B, C, and tumble-down D.

Karen's Opposites

I am happy.
I am sad.

I am good.
I am bad.

I am in.
I am out.

This is a whisper.
This is a shout.

My dog is black.
My cat is white.

If this hand is left,
which foot is right?

One is short.
One is tall.

Why are there none?
I have them all.

These are hot.   These are cold.

We are young.   We are old.

Up here is the sky.

Down here is the ground.

My ball is lost. Look what I've found!

A Kitten with a Mitten

A kitten with a mitten on
  Never did I see.
A kitten with a mitten on
  Would never ever be.

A kitten with a mitten on
  Should stay out of the snow.
A kitten needs FOUR mittens on.
  I'm old enough to know.

Choosing a Kitten

A black-nosed kitten
Will slumber all the day.

A white-nosed kitten
Is ever glad to play.

A yellow-nosed kitten
Will answer to your call.

And a gray-nosed kitten
I like best of all.

I Like Dogs

I like dogs—
Big dogs
Little dogs
Fat dogs
Doggy dogs
Old dogs
Puppy dogs.

I like dogs—
A dog that is barking
over the hill,
A dog that is dreaming
very still,
A dog that is running
wherever he will.
I like dogs.

I Like Flies

I like flies—
May flies
Fire flies
Bottle flies
Butterflies.
I like flies.

I like flies—
Black flies
Green flies
Mean flies
Any kind of fly.

A fly busy buzzing,
A fly sitting still,
A fly in a hurry
flying over a hill—

I like flies.

The Seven Weathers

One day a little dog
had to stay indoors.
He hated
to get his feet wet.

That day it rained

and it snowed

and the fog rolled in

and the fog melted

and there was a wind

and a storm

and a breeze

and a shower.

Then the sun came out
and all the flowers came up
because it was spring.

And then the sun shone
and the little dog went out
to take a walk before night
on his four soft feet,
just in time—

Because
then the stars came out
and it was night.
And the wind began to blow
all sorts of
lovely evening smells
to his nose.

New Shoes

Here we go,
In ones and twos,
Down the street
In our new shoes.

Some are brown,
And some are black.
Some go fast
And some turn back.

Some are red,
And some are blue.
Some go squeaking,
(Some shoes do),

Some go skip,
And some go hop.
Here's the corner—
All shoes stop!

STOP

All the cars
Go by, and then,
On our way
We go again,

Here and there,
In ones and twos,
Down the street
In our new shoes.

Animal Talk

Animal talk is lion talk,
The talking of the deer.
Animal talk is rabbit talk.
Listen and you'll hear.

Animal talk is kitten talk,
The talking of the birds.
Animal talk is story talk.
Look, you'll see their words.

Good Morning

One day I saw
a downy duck,
With feathers
on his back.

I said,
"Good morning,
downy duck,"
And he said,
"Quack,
quack,
quack."

One day I saw
a scarlet bird.
He woke me
from my sleep.

I said,
"Good-morning,
scarlet bird,"
And he said,
  "Cheep,
      cheep,
          cheep."

Snow! Snow! Snow!

"Snow, snow, snow!"
said Henny Hen.
"I wish winter was far away."

"Do you, Henny?"
said Jack Rabbit.
"Do you want spring to be here?"

"Yes, I do," said Henny Hen.
"But in spring there is
rain, rain, rain."

"Rain in spring!"
said Jack Rabbit.
"Do you wish spring was far away?
Do you want summer to be here?"

"Yes, I do," said Henny Hen.
"But in summer there is
dust, dust, dust."

"Dust in summer!"
said Jack Rabbit.
"Do you wish summer
was far away?
Do you want fall to be here?"

"Yes I do!" said Henny Hen.
"But in fall there are
leaves, leaves, leaves."

Jack Rabbit said,
"Leaves in the fall!
Do you want fall
to be far away, Henny?"

"Yes, I do!" said Henny.
"Then you want winter
and snow, snow, snow,"
said Jack Rabbit.

Henny said, "Yes, I do!"
Henny sang, "Snow, snow,
beautiful snow!"
Jack Rabbit sang, "Snow, snow,
beautiful snow!"

Henny and Jack sang,
"Snow, snow, beautiful snow."
And they danced in the snow,
the beautiful snow.

A Song for the King

Lion was king of all the animals.
King Lion loved music.
"Who will sing for me?"
King Lion asked all the animals.
"I shall sing for you," said Pink Pig.
Pink Pig sang and sang.
He sang, "Oink, oink, oink!"

"Thank you for your song,"
said the king.
"But it was not quite
what I had in mind."

Along came White Sheep.
"I shall sing for the king,"
said White Sheep.
White Sheep sang and sang.
He sang, "Baa, baa, baa!"

"Thank you," said King Lion.
"Thank you for your song.
But it is not quite
what I had in mind."

Along came Yellow Bird.

"Let me sing for you, King Lion,"
said Yellow Bird.

He sang and sang.

He sang, "Chirp, chirp!"

He sang, "Cheep, cheep!"

He sang, "Cheer, cheer!"

"Thank you," said the king.
"Thank you, Yellow Bird.
That is a lovely song.
That is lovely music.
And it is just what I had in mind."

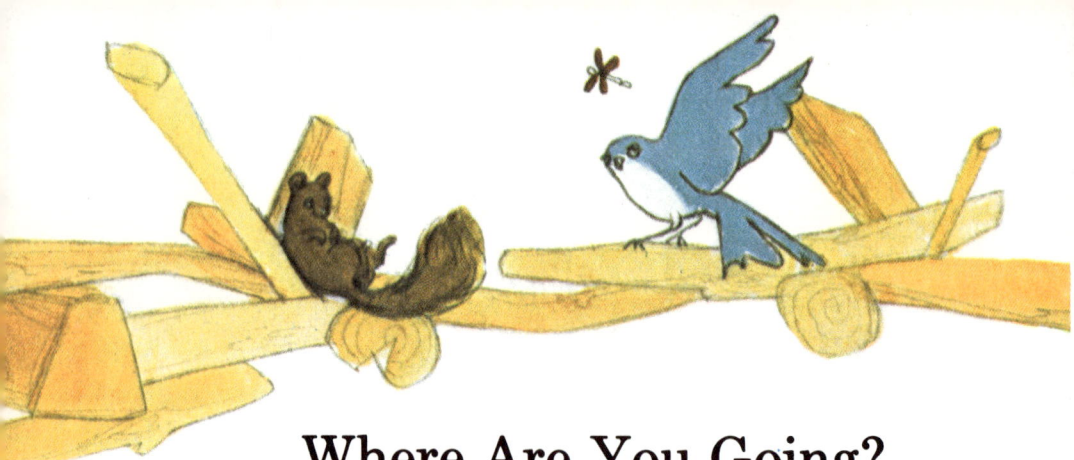

Where Are You Going?

"Where are you going,
  you little pig?"
"I'm leaving my mother,
I'm growing so big."

"So big, young pig?
  So young, so big?
What, leaving your mother,
you foolish young pig!"

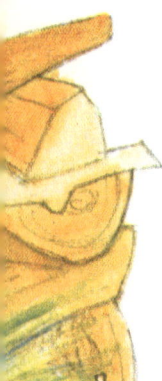

"Where are you going,
   you little pig?"
"I've got a new spade,
and I'm going to dig."

"To dig, little pig?
   A little pig dig?
Well, I never saw a pig
with a spade that could dig!"

"Where are you going,
  you little pig?"
"I'm going to the barber's
to buy me a wig."

"A wig, little pig?
  A pig in a wig?
Whoever saw a pig in a wig!"

The Frog on the Log

There once
Was a green
Little frog, frog, frog—

Who played
In the wood
On a log, log, log!

A screech owl
Sitting
In a tree, tree, tree—

Came after
The frog
With a scree, scree, scree!

When the frog
Heard the owl—
In a flash, flash, flash—

He leaped
In the pond
With a splash, splash, splash!

Meow

"Meow!" said the cat.
Sandy opened the door
to let the cat out.

"Meow!" said the cat.
Sandy opened the door
to let the cat in.

"Meow!" said the cat.

Sandy gave the cat
a saucer of milk.

"It's nice to be a cat,"
Sandy said.
"You just say *meow*
and people do what you want.
I think I will be a cat."

"Meow!" said Sandy.

"Are you a cat?"
asked Sandy's mother.
"Meow!" said Sandy.
"You are a cat,"
said Mother.

"I am going to the store.
I do not know if
I should take a cat with me."
"Meow!" said Sandy.

"Well," said his mother,
"I will try.
But do not jump
on the counters.
Do not chase mice.
Do not run away."

"Meow!" said Sandy.

At the supermarket,
Sandy met Johnny.
"Hello, Sandy," said Johnny.
"Meow!" said Sandy.
"He's a cat,"
said Sandy's mother.

"Oh," said Johnny.
"Can I be a cat, too?"
"Ask your mother,"
said Sandy's mother.

They went to the drugstore.
Sandy walked over
to the soda fountain.
"Meow!" said Sandy.

"Is he a cat?"
asked the soda fountain man.
"He is a cat,"
said Sandy's mother.

"Meow!" said Sandy.

"I think he wants something,"
said the soda fountain man.
"Maybe your cat
wants some ice cream."
"Maybe he does,"
said Sandy's mother.
"Give him
a chocolate ice cream cone."

Before the man could get it,
Sandy said,
"I do not like chocolate.
I like vanilla."

"Which *meow* means vanilla?
Which *meow* means chocolate?"
asked Sandy's mother.

"I don't know," said Sandy.
"I think I will be a boy again."

So Sandy was a boy again,
and he had his vanilla
ice cream cone.
It was good, too!

Story People

Story people
Have a way
Of knowing what
To do and say.

So come along,
And don't be slow.
We'll go where
Story people go!

The Teeny Tiny Woman

Once there was
a teeny tiny woman.
She lived
in a teeny tiny house.

One day she put on
her teeny tiny hat.
She took a teeny tiny walk.
She came
to a teeny tiny garden.

In the teeny tiny garden
was a teeny tiny scarecrow!
It had on a teeny tiny hat
and a teeny tiny dress.

The teeny tiny woman said,
"That teeny tiny hat
and that teeny tiny dress
will fit teeny tiny me."

She took them home
and put them
in her teeny tiny closet.

Then she took
a teeny tiny nap
on her teeny tiny bed.

A teeny tiny voice
from the teeny tiny closet said,

"Give me my hat!
Give me my dress!"

The teeny tiny woman
was a teeny tiny bit afraid.
She put her teeny tiny head
under her teeny tiny covers.

Then the teeny tiny voice
said a teeny tiny bit louder,

"Give me my hat!

Give me my dress!"

The teeny tiny woman was
a teeny tiny bit more afraid.
She put her teeny tiny head
down a teeny tiny bit more
under the covers.

The teeny tiny voice
from the teeny tiny closet
said a teeny tiny bit louder,
"Give me my hat!
Give me my dress!"

Then the teeny tiny woman
sat up in her teeny tiny bed.
She said in her loudest
teeny tiny voice,
"Take them!"

Penny Whistle

Once there was a little boy.
He lived in a mud hut,
near the jungle.

He had no brothers
or sisters.
He had no bats or balls.
He had no toys.
He was very lonely.

One day his father
went to market.
He bought a penny whistle
for the little boy.

The little boy wasn't lonely
any more.
He blew the whistle
over and over
all day long, until . . .
his mother called him
Penny Whistle.

He blew the same tune
over and over, until . . .
his father shouted,
"Stop that noise!"

Penny Whistle
went for a walk
in the jungle
to find a new tune.
He walked along,
blowing his whistle,
the same tune,
over and over.

The jungle was full of birds—
   big birds,
   little birds,
   light birds,
   bright birds.

The birds were singing,
   high and low,
   loud and soft.

"I can do that, too,"
said Penny Whistle.

He blew a new tune
on his penny whistle.
He blew his whistle
high and low,
loud and soft.

Penny Whistle walked home
through the jungle,
blowing his whistle.
He blew his new tune,
    high and low,
    loud and soft.

His father shouted,
"Good for you,
Penny Whistle.
Now you whistle
like a bird."

Shadows

When I wake up
on a sunny morning,
my shadow wakes up
with me.

I know
this will be a good day,
a fine sunny day
for shadows
and shadow games.

We have plenty of things to do.
And wherever we go,
our tag-along shadows
go with us.

Shadows, shadows, shadows.
Tree shadows on the grass.

Grass shadows on the trees.

People shadows,
dog shadows,
balloon shadows.

Bug shadows,

flower shadows,
butterfly shadows.

But where do all the shadows go
when it rains?

We go home to play,
and my mother turns on the light.

There is my shadow
waiting for me.

So we do shadow tricks
all afternoon.
And we have a shadow parade.

In My Mother's House

This is my Mother's house.
My Father made it.
He made it strong.

He made it big.
He made it high.
My Mother's house,
I live in it.

In my Mother's house
all day
I play and work.
All night
I sleep.

The walls come close around me
in a good way.

I can see them.
I can feel them.
I live with them.

This house is good to me.
It keeps me.
I like it,
my Mother's house.

My Mother's house,
it does not stand alone.
Its sister houses
are all around it.

We are the people
living together,
all of us together.

We live here
in the houses,
together.

When it is dark,
all of us are sleeping.

When it is day,
we are working,
always
together.

It is good to stand close
like our houses.

The Alphabet

C is a clown, and M is me
  And K is a kangaroo.
I like the names of things I see,
  So I like letters, too.

Alphabet of Words

I like arrow,
and apple,
and ape.

I like **Aa**

I like bumblebee,
bouncing,
and bed.

I like **Bb**

I like color,
and cooky,
and clown.

I like

I like digging,
and dancing,
and duck.

I like

I like elephant,
eagle,
and elf.

I like  **Ee**

I'm fond of fishing
and finding frogs.

I like **Ff**

I'm glad to gallop
on good green grass.

I like **Gg**

I'm happy for hills,
and horses,
and hiding.

I like **Hh**

I don't like itches,
but since I'm an Indian,

I like **Ii**

I jump for joy
about jingle
and jangle.

I like **Jj**

I like kangaroo,
kitten,
and key.

I like **Kk**

I like lion,
and leaping,
and lamb.

I like **Ll**

I like music,
and monkey,
and mouse.

I like **Mm**

I like numbers,
and nests,
and noise.

I like **Nn**

I like orange,
and otter,
and owl.

I like Oo

I like ping-pong,
and penguin,
and paint.

I like Pp

I like queen,
and question,
and quack.

I like **Qq**

I like rainbow
and ready-to-go.

I like **Rr**

I like secret,
and skating,
and sliding.

I like **Ss**

I like tiptoe,
and tickle,
and turtle.

I like **Tt**

I like under,
umbrella,
and up.

I like **Uu**

I like violin,
violet,
and voice.

I like **Vv**

I like whisper,
and winking,
and wing.

I like **Ww**

I like x-ray,
what else can I say?

I like **Xx**

I like yellow,
and yo-yo,
and yak.

I like Yy

I like zebra,
and zipper,
and zing!

I like Zz

Hello and Good-by

Hello and Good-by
Met today,
And this is what
I heard them say:

"Hello, Good-by."
"Hello, Hello."
"Good-by, Good-by."
"Good-by, Hello."

ACKNOWLEDGMENTS

The editors wish to extend their thanks and appreciation to the following authors, publishers, and periodicals for kindly granting us permission to reprint selections in this volume.

THE ASSOCIATION FOR CHILDHOOD EDUCATION INTERNATIONAL for GOOD MORNING by Muriel Sipe Ross from *Sung Under the Silver Umbrella*, copyright 1935 by The Macmillan Company. —ERICK BERRY for PENNY WHISTLE adapted from *Penny Whistle* by Erick Berry, copyright 1930 by The Macmillan Co., Inc. —CURTIS PUBLISHING COMPANY, INC. for HELLO and GOODBYE by James Steel Smith from *Jack and Jill Magazine*, copyright 1948 by Curtis Publishing Company, Inc. —E. P. DUTTON, INC. for SEESAW from *Another Here and Now Story Book* by Evelyn Beyer, copyright 1937 by E. P. Dutton, Inc. —GARRET & MASSIE, INC. for ON TOP from *Moods and Moments* by Lindley J. Stiles, copyright 1955 by Lindley J. Stiles. —GOLDEN PRESS, INC. for the following, copyrighted in the years indicated by Golden Press, Inc.: I LIKE DOGS from *The Golden Friendly Book* by Margaret Wise Brown (1954); I LIKE FLIES and THE SEVEN WEATHERS from *The Wonderful Story Book* by Margaret Wise Brown (1948); A SONG FOR THE KING from *Dogs and Cats, Birds and Bats*, a Merrigold Book by Adelaide Holl (1964); NEW SHOES and an adaptation of SNOW! SNOW! SNOW! from *The Golden Book of 365 Stories* by Kathryn Jackson (1955); TWENTY'S PLENTY, an excerpt from "Ducklings" in *Farm Stories* by Kathryn and Byron Jackson (1946); BALLS by Edith Osswald from *The Little Golden Book of Toys* (1945); and KAREN'S OPPOSITES from *Karen's Opposites* by Alice and Martin Provensen (1963). —HARCOURT, BRACE & WORLD, INC. for SHADOWS from *The Shadow Book* by Beatrice Schenk de Regniers and Isabel Gordon, copyright 1960 by Beatrice Schenk de Regniers; and SLIDING from *Whispers and Other Poems* by Myra Cohn Livingston, copyright 1958 by Myra Cohn Livingston. —HART PUBLISHING COMPANY, INC. for I WISH I WERE A RABBIT from *A Treasury of Songs* by Esther Botwin, copyright 1954 by Hart Publishing Company, Inc. —HUMPTY DUMPTY'S MAGAZINE for MEOW by Harold Longman, copyright 1964 by Parents Magazine Enterprises, Inc. —DAVID MCKAY COMPANY, INC. for SNOWY MORNING from *Christopher O!* by Barbara Young, copyright 1947 by Barbara Young. —HUGHES MEARNS estate for THE LITTLE MAN WHO WASN'T THERE by Hughes Mearns. —CHARLES E. MERRILL BOOKS, INC. and ARTISTS AND WRITERS PRESS, INC. for BOX FUN by Patricia and Richard Scarry, copyright 1960 by Charles E. Merrill Books, Inc., and Artists and Writers Press, Inc. —CHARLES E. MERRILL BOOKS, INC. for THE TEENY TINY WOMAN by Mildred L. Kerr and Frances Ross, from *First Fairy Tales*, copyright 1946 by Charles E. Merrill Books, Inc. —MRS. ILO ORLEANS for THE FROG ON THE LOG from *The Zoo That Grew* by Ilo Orleans, published by Henry Z. Walck, Inc., copyright 1960 by Ilo Orleans; I WISH I HAD by Ilo Orleans; THE NECK by Ilo Orleans from *Child Life Magazine*, copyright 1951 by Ilo Orleans. —THE SOCIETY OF AUTHORS for JUMPS by Rose Fyleman. —THE VIKING PRESS, INC. for excerpts from IN MY MOTHER'S HOUSE by Ann Nolan Clark, copyright 1941 by Ann Nolan Clark. —FREDERICK WARNE & COMPANY, INC. for JUMPING from *Marigold Garden* by Kate Greenaway, copyright 1910 by Frederick Warne & Company, Inc.